# READ WELL®

# Communities

## UNITS 5-7

5  6  7  8  9    RRD    14  13  12  11  10

Read Well is a registered trademark of Sopris West Educational Services.

ISBN 978-1-60218-551-7
ISBN 1-60218-551-4

Printed in the United States of America
Published and Distributed by

## Cambium
LEARNING®
Sopris West®

4093 Specialty Place • Longmont, CO 80504 • (303) 651-2829
www.sopriswest.com

167257/1-10

# UNIT 5
# Life as an Ant

# Ant Communities

*by Lucy Bledsoe*
*adapted by Ann Watanabe*
*and Karen Akiyama-Paik*

### K-W-L
### (modified)

| Ants | | |
|---|---|---|
| What do we think we <u>k</u>now? | What do we <u>w</u>ant to know? | What did we <u>l</u>earn? |

**Chapters 1, 2**

# Vocabulary

### ★ sur·vive

**Survive** means to stay alive.

People need food and water to *survive*. What do you think animals need to survive?

### hab·i·tat

The place where an animal or plant lives and grows is called its **habitat**.

A hippo's *habitat* is near rivers in Africa. What is a shark's habitat?

★ = New

### ★ ex·cept

**Except** is a short way of saying "everything but" or "everywhere but."

I like all vegetables *except* broccoli. Do I like broccoli? Complete this sentence: I like to eat everything . . .

### ★ com·mu·ni·ty

A **community** is a group of people or animals that lives and works together.

Our school is a *community*. Why is our school a community?

### ★ col·o·ny

A **colony** is a group of animals that lives together.

Complete this sentence: Thousands of ants live together in a . . .

## Chapter 1

# Ant Facts

**Ant Anatomy**

Did you know that ants are insects?  Like all insects, they have six legs and three main body parts. All ants have a head, a thorax, and an abdomen. Ants also have antennas on their heads.  Antennas help them hear, taste, and smell.

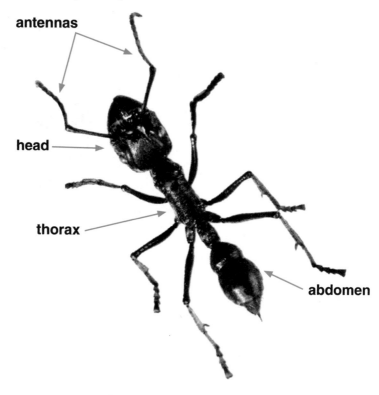

Touch the antennas . . . the head . . . the thorax . . . and the abdomen.  How do you know an ant is an insect?

## Survivors

There are around 20,000 different kinds of ants. These amazing insects have been on Earth for millions of years. Ants have been on Earth since the dinosaurs. They can survive in any habitat except where it is frozen year round.

Like all living things, ants need other living things to survive. Just like people, these tiny insects live and work together in communities.

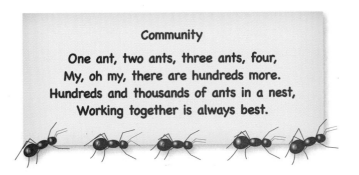

**Community**
One ant, two ants, three ants, four,
My, oh my, there are hundreds more.
Hundreds and thousands of ants in a nest,
Working together is always best.

What are some facts that make an ant an *amazing* animal?

## Chapter 2

# Colonies

What do you know about ant anatomy? What facts make these insects amazing animals?

Ants live and work together in communities called colonies. Thousands of ants may live in one colony.

### The Nest

If you see a trail of ants, they may be on their way to their front door. The ant colony lives in a nest. The nest is like an underground apartment building with many rooms. These rooms are called chambers.

Look at the picture. Where do ants live? Where do you think the trail of ants will lead?

The nest has special chambers for different things—storerooms for food, nurseries for baby ants, rooms for resting, and rooms for trash. The queen ant has her own chamber.

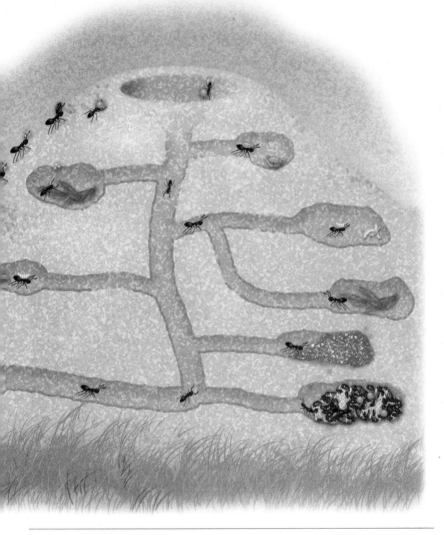

Why do you think the queen has her own special chamber?

### The Queen of the Colony

Most colonies have one queen. The queen ant is the biggest ant in the colony. Worker ants build a nest for her. The workers feed, guard, and even bathe her.

The queen's job is to lay tiny eggs. Each egg is as small as a grain of sand. Most of the eggs will hatch into female ants. Females are the workers, so many female ants are needed for the colony to survive.

What is the queen's job? How do the workers take care of the queen? Why are most ants females?

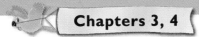

**Chapters 3, 4**

# Vocabulary

★ **life cy·cle**

From birth to death, plants and animals go through changes. These changes, or stages, are called a **life cycle**.

Look at the picture. What are the four stages in the *life cycle* of a butterfly?

★ **met·a·mor·pho·sis**

**Metamorphosis** is a big change that some animals go through during their life cycle.

What is a *metamorphosis*? Complete this sentence: A tadpole goes through a metamorphosis by changing from a tadpole into a . . .

★ **molt**

When animals shed their skin, they **molt**.

Snakes and caterpillars *molt*. When a snake molts, what happens?

★ **pro·tect**

**Protect** means to keep safe.

Mother animals *protect* their babies. What do mother gorillas do?

★ = New

Chapter 3

# Life Cycle

What do you know about ant colonies and the queen ant? What will you learn about in this chapter?

___

## The Four Stages

Each ant has four stages in its life:

## Life Cycle of Ants

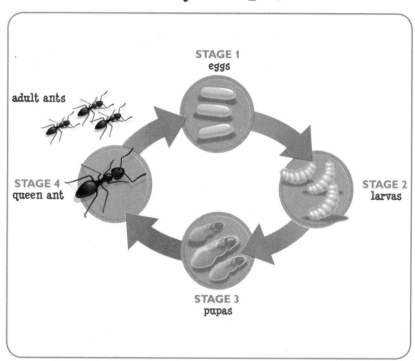

▲ Like butterflies and frogs, ants go through a big change called a *metamorphosis*.

___

Using the diagram above, describe the *life cycle* of ants.

## STAGE 1
### eggs

As soon as the queen lays her eggs, worker ants carry the eggs to the nursery. The eggs must be kept at the right temperature, so the nursery workers move the eggs to different chambers several times a day.

## STAGE 2
### larvas

When the eggs hatch, the baby ants look like tiny worms called larvas. The worker ants clean the larvas and keep them warm by moving them to different chambers. The workers even feed the babies food from their own stomachs.

As the larvas grow, their skin gets tight. They shed their skin and grow new skin. This is called molting. The larvas molt four or five times during this stage.

What happens to the eggs after the queen ant lays them? How do the workers take care of the larvas? Why do the larvas molt?

## STAGE 3
### pupas

During the third stage, the larvas spin cocoons around their bodies. Now the baby ants are called pupas. The pupas grow inside their cocoons. The workers also move the pupas to different chambers several times a day.

## STAGE 4
### adults

When the pupas have changed into adults, worker ants bite open the cocoons. During this fourth stage, the new adult ants crawl out. Soon they will be strong and ready to do their jobs within the colony.

What happens in stage 3? Why do you think the worker ants move the pupas to different chambers? What happens in stage 4?

## Chapter 4

# Working Together

### A Community of Workers

It takes a community of workers to care for an ant colony. Ants do many jobs:

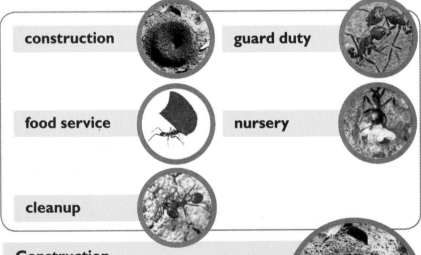

construction

guard duty

food service

nursery

cleanup

### Construction

Ants that do construction work use their jaws to dig out chambers and tunnels in the nest. Have you ever seen an anthill? Construction workers carry the extra dirt out of the chambers, making a hill of dirt above the nest.

Name five jobs that worker ants do. Describe what a construction worker does.

## Food Service

Many workers are needed to gather food. Finding food is dangerous because the ants must leave the safety of their nest. Some ants hunt. Some collect seeds and sweet liquids from plants. Ants look for food wherever it can be found.

Ants wave their antennas in the air looking for food. When an ant finds food, it returns to the nest, dragging its body on the ground. This makes a smelly path that other ants can follow.

Describe what worker ants do to find food.

20

Ants drag big chunks of food back to their nest. Little ants are amazingly strong. They can lift 10 times their own weight!

## Cleanup

Some workers clean the nest, taking unused food and even dead ants to the nest's dump. The dump may be inside or outside the nest.

Describe what is happening in the picture. Could you walk home with a bag full of groceries that weighed as much as 10 of your friends?

## Guard Duty

Some worker ants protect
the nest. They stand near the
entrance to watch out for other
animals and ants that don't belong.

If danger is near, these ants let out a strong smell
to warn the other ants. Ants on guard duty may even
attack enemies.

## Nursery

Nursery workers take care of
the eggs, larvas, and pupas by
keeping them warm and well fed.

## Busy Communities

Tiny ant communities are busy, busy places.
Every ant has a job.

If you were an ant, what job would
you want?

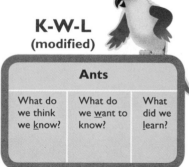

**K-W-L**
(modified)

| Ants | | |
|---|---|---|
| What do we think we know? | What do we want to know? | What did we learn? |

# An Ant With Ideas

by Paula Rich

illustrated by David Opie

Look at the picture. Which ant do you think is the main character? What makes you think the first ant is the main character? What do you know about that ant already?

Chapters 1–3

# Vocabulary

## ★ i·ma·gi·na·tion

If you can think of new ideas or stories, you have **imagination**.

Inventors have great *imagination*. Use your imagination and tell me what you think our next story will be about.

## ★ trea·sure

A **treasure** is something valuable or important. A treasure is often money, jewels, or gold, but it can be anything you think is important.

The pirate's *treasure* was a chest of gold. My treasure is a baseball card. Why is it a treasure?

## ★ daw·dle

**Dawdle** means to do something slowly.

Sometimes, I stop and look at things on my way to school. Sometimes, I *dawdle* on my way to school. What's another way to say, "Sometimes, I take my time when I get ready for school"? Start with "Sometimes, I . . ."

★ = New

★ **col·lapse**

> **Collapse** means to fall down suddenly and completely.
>
> What's another way to say, "We built a tower of blocks, but it fell down"?

★ **im·pressed**

> To be **impressed** means to think someone does something really well.
>
> Tim was *impressed* with Maria's new magic trick. What is something you are impressed with?

# Chapter 1

# Cleanup Worker

What kind of ant is this chapter going to be about?

Antonia liked living next to the big red house. The grass was thick and green. The dirt was rich, black, and easy to dig. There were lots of mouth-watering insects to eat. But Antonia liked the trash cans best. Her nest was right beside them. Such wonderful things fell out of the cans! She found not only sweet food, but things that made her imagination fly.

Who is the main character? Describe Antonia.

Purple buttons, a matchbox, a drinking straw, marbles that swirled with color—why did the people in the big red house throw out such interesting things? Antonia kept her treasures in a deep crack in the sidewalk behind the cans.

Antonia was a cleanup worker. All day, she marched in a line with her sisters, taking leftover food out of the dark cool nest into the bright sunshine of the outside world. As they worked, she kept an eye out for more treasures around the trash cans. When she slowed down to look, her sisters would tell her, "Back to work, Antonia! No time to dawdle!"

What makes Antonia an interesting ant? What are the things Antonia thinks are *treasures*? Why do you think Antonia *dawdles*?

## Chapter 2

# Antonia's Ideas

All day long, Antonia helped her sisters clean the nest. But when the ants marched out into the world, Antonia kept her eye out for treasures near the trash cans.

Antonia liked her job as a cleanup worker, but she really wanted to be a construction worker. After all, an ant with ideas should be in construction!

One time, Antonia had an idea to put a pretty marble on top of their nest. She thought that if any other ants attacked their nest, she and her sisters could roll the marble down the nest hill to stop them. But the marble rolled off by accident one day, and 27 of her sisters ended up in the hospital.

How did Antonia think the marble could be used? What was the problem? Why did Antonia think she should be a construction worker?

Then Antonia had an idea to put the purple buttons on the matchbox, like wheels on a cart. It would be useful for moving the baby ants around, she thought. But the matchbox cart got stuck in the tight turns of the nest's tunnels. And the baby ants got carsick.

"No more ideas!" her sisters said. "Back to work! No time to dawdle!"

Why didn't the matchbox cart work? Do you think Antonia should stick to her job as a cleanup worker? Why or why not?

# Chapter 3

# A Good Idea

Describe some of Antonia's ideas.  What do you think is going to happen in this chapter?

The Queen was going to start laying eggs very soon, and the ant colony needed a new nursery.  The nursery had to be warm in the winter and cool in the summer.  It had to be down deep in the ground.

Building the new nursery was a hard job for the construction workers.  Dirt had to be carried a long way out of the nest.  One of the tunnels kept collapsing.

Why are the construction workers building a new nursery?  What problems are they having?

As the cleanup workers marched past the construction zone, Antonia had an idea. She stopped suddenly. The line of ants behind her zigged and zagged as her sisters ran into each other. They didn't like that.

"There's so much work to do!" they cried. Their antennas waggled up and down when they were excited. "Let's get going! We've got to clean the Queen's chamber, and the sleeping chambers, and the tunnels! No time to dawdle!"

But Antonia wanted to help the construction team. She had an idea! The drinking straw—it was sturdy and round. An ant could walk through it.

"How about using a straw to hold up the tunnel roof?" Antonia asked.

How did Antonia want to help the construction crew? How could the straw help them with the tunnel that kept *collapsing?*

At first the construction workers laughed. But then the crew leader said, "Time's getting short! Let's try Antonia's idea."

So Antonia and 10 of the strongest workers got the straw from the crack in the sidewalk. They pushed and pulled it down to the collapsing tunnel. It worked! The tunnel roof stayed up.

The crew leader was impressed. Antonia's invention made the work go much faster. "An ant with ideas should be in construction!" the crew leader said. "Let's get to work, Antonia! No time to dawdle!"

Soon the Queen had a beautiful new nursery. Antonia was proud to be part of the construction team. She couldn't wait for their next job, because she had more treasures and more ideas to share!

---

Close your eyes. Imagine a straw in the ants' nest. How are the ants using the straw? Why was the leader of the construction crew *impressed* with Antonia?

# Fluency

## The Lost Treasure
*by Paula Rich*
*illustrated by David Opie*

Antonia's new treasure was lost. She     6
looked everywhere for it. She ran down all the     15
tunnels of the nest. She stopped at every room     24
and stuck her head inside. She wiggled her     32
antennas to pick up a smell. It wasn't in the     42
food storage rooms or in the sleeping chambers.     50
She didn't see or smell it in any of the nurseries.     61
She went into the hospital and crawled     68
underneath all the beds. She even looked in the     77
trash chambers—yuck!     80

Finally, Antonia     82
came to the Queen's     86
chamber. There it was—     90
the dark blue hatpin!     94
The Queen thought it     98
was beautiful. Antonia     101
was happy to give her     106
treasure to the Queen.     110

At the beginning of the story, how did Antonia feel? How could you tell?
What did she do to solve her problem? Do you think Antonia may have felt
*bittersweet* at the end? If so, why?

## UNIT 6
# Sir Henry

# Sir Henry

*by Ann Watanabe and Marilyn Sprick*
*illustrated by Janet Pederson*

This is a story about a *community*. Who is part of the community?

### Chapters 1, 2

# Vocabulary

## ★ lo·cal

**Local** describes things and places close to your home or community.

A *local* school is a school close to your home. What do you call a bank that is close to your home?

## ★ com·mo·tion

A **commotion** is a lot of noise and activity.

Dad did not like the *commotion* we made with our music. Describe the commotion.

## ★ de·light·ful

**Delightful** means cheerful and fun.

He is a *delightful* child. Describe the child.

★ = New

### ★ vic·to·ry

A **victory** is a win.

When the girl won the race, it was a sweet *victory*.

### com·mu·ni·ty

A **community** is a group of people or animals that lives and works together.

Most people live together in a *community*. The story of Sir Henry is about a community. Name someone who lives in your community.

### ★ con·grat·u·late

**Congratulate** means to tell others you are happy for them because they won something or did something special.

The principal *congratulated* the student for reading 100 books. If someone wins a race, what will we do?

Chapter 1

# No Ordinary Day

Look at the pictures and think about the chapter title.
What do you think is going to happen in this chapter?

It was exactly 6:00 a.m. I could hear the garbage trucks outside my window. I crawled out from under the bed.

I was so excited! This was no ordinary day. John, Mom, and Dad were checking to see that everything on our list was packed. I was ready!

I had won the local contest and was going to the state contest. The living room was full of balloons and treats. My trainer, the kids next door, the grocery clerk, and the florist with flowers all arrived at the same time to send me off.

What makes a community? People in **communities** cheer each other on.

What kind of day is it? What do you think the family is doing?

I loved all the commotion. Every once in a while, someone would pat me on the head and say, "Good job."

John looked a little nervous.

At exactly 9:00 a.m., we were ready to go. Mom threw my scarf around my neck. Dad helped me with my goggles. Soon we were on our way to Orlando and the state contest.

Who is telling the story? There are two clues that tell you who is talking. What are the clues?

## Chapter 2

# Local Dog Wins

**WEATHER**
Sunny with a chance of showers in the afternoon. Cool overnight.

# Jollytown Gazette

**FINAL EDITION**
DOG SHOW EXCLUSIVE

## Local Dog Wins Best in Show at State Contest

by George Page, reporter

Sir Henry White wowed the crowd and judges at the state contest—winning Best in Show. The judge exclaimed, "Just delightful! This dog is a true winner."

Sir Henry's owner, John White, beamed.

John White's parents said, "We are thankful for everyone's support."

John read a thank-you note to the community. "Sir Henry and I want to thank you all for your help. We especially want to thank Groomer's Delight and Sir Henry's vet and trainers. This victory belongs to many people."

What did Sir Henry win? Who did Sir Henry and John thank?

When we got home, John and I took a long walk through the neighborhood. Everywhere we went, people congratulated us. I carried the trophy with me. The firefighters let me sit on their truck so they could get a picture of me.

When we got to the pet store, the owner gave me a bone. John carefully put the trophy where I could watch it while I chewed on the bone.

Why did everyone in the neighborhood *congratulate* Sir Henry? How did Sir Henry feel about his trophy? How can you tell?

As soon as the kids in the park saw us, they dashed over to see us. They admired the trophy.

Even the groundskeeper stopped mowing the lawn to congratulate us. John and I took a long victory walk through the neighborhood. Before going home, we stopped and talked at the butcher shop, the bakery, and the police station. I was famous!

Your community is the group of people who lives and works in your neighborhood.

Sir Henry and John took a *victory* walk through the neighborhood. What do you think a victory walk is? People in the *community* congratulated Sir Henry. Who were some of these people?

**Chapters 3, 4**

# Vocabulary

★ **plead**

**Plead** means to beg. When you really want something, you may beg, or plead, for it.

The boy *pleaded* with his mom to let him stay up late. Have you ever begged, or pleaded, for something? What was it?

★ **dis·tressed**

**Distressed** means very upset.

The girl was *distressed* when she lost her dog. Have you ever been very upset and worried? What were you distressed about?

★ **ex·haust·ed**

**Exhausted** means very tired.

The baby was *exhausted* after visiting the relatives. Show me what you would look like if you were exhausted.

★ **re·trace**

**Retrace** means to go back and do something again. When you retrace your steps, you go back exactly the way you came.

I lost my ring and *retraced* my steps to find it. If you lost your pencil on the way to the library, what should you do?

 ★ = New

## Chapter 3

# A Distressing Day

WEATHER
Mostly cloudy with
75 percent chance of
thunderstorms by evening.

**Jollytown Gazette** FINAL EDITION

DOG SHOW EXCLUSIVE

## Show Trophy Disappears

### by George Page, reporter

This morning, Police Officer Wong of the Jollytown police reported, "Sir Henry White's Best in Show Trophy has disappeared."

Owner John White was speechless and had no comment. John's parents pleaded to people in the community, "Please call if you have any information about the missing trophy. Sir Henry is quite distressed. He is moody and will not come out of the corner."

Officer Wong said, "Anyone with information on the missing trophy should call the Doggie Help Hotline."

---

What is the problem? What did John's parents ask the people in the community to do? Why?

I could not believe that my trophy was gone.

I went to bed that night without eating. I had lost my appetite. John tried to help. He said, "Don't worry, Sir Henry. Officer Wong has called on community volunteers to help find your trophy. We will leave no stone unturned."

John told Sir Henry that the community volunteers would leave no stone unturned. What does that mean?

## Chapter 4

# The Search

It seemed like the whole community showed up to search for my trophy. There were a lot of people—the butcher, the baker, and the neighborhood kids. The barber, my groomer, my trainer, the florist, and the librarian all showed up. Some were old friends and some were new neighbors. I was impressed!

Officer Wong took charge. She gathered everyone together and gave each group a map. Everyone studied their maps. One group spoke in Spanish, another in German, and others just spoke plain ordinary English. There was no doubt in my mind that they all wanted to help.

Who is helping to look for the trophy? Why is Sir Henry impressed by the search for his trophy?

Officer Wong told John and me to retrace our steps. The victory walk in the neighborhood was the last time we had the trophy.

Here's the map that John and I used.

We walked, and walked, and walked.

1 The trophy was not at the fire station.
2 The trophy was not at the pet store.
3 The trophy was not at the park.
4 The trophy was not at the butcher's shop or the bakery.
5 Our last stop was the police station.

Where did John and Sir Henry look for the trophy? Let's *retrace* their steps on the map.

We were exhausted. With our heads hanging low, we dragged ourselves into the station.

Twelve beautiful orange roses sat on the clerk's desk. I started to admire the flowers when . . . I heard myself bark.

Oh, my! I couldn't believe my eyes! The roses were sitting in my trophy!

What did Sir Henry do when he saw the orange roses? What were the roses in? Was Sir Henry's problem solved? There is still a mystery. What is it?

## Chapters 5, 6

# Vocabulary

## pop·u·lar

Something is **popular** when many people like it.

Our local restaurant is very *popular*. What do you know about the restaurant?

## ★ sulk

**Sulk** means to show that you are unhappy. People often sulk by pouting and not talking.

Mom said that we could not stay up late. We were so unhappy that we *sulked*. What do some kids do when they can't have their way?

### Idioms and Expressions

## ★ chain of e·vents

A **chain of events** is a series of things that happen in a certain order. Each thing causes the next thing to happen.

Minnie Bird screeched. Miss Tam jumped and spilled the milk. Old Scraggly Cat walked through the milk and left paw prints all over the house. What was the *chain of events*?

## ★ = New

49

## Chapter 5

# Problem Solved

What's the mystery? What do you hope to learn in this chapter?

---

WEATHER
Clear skies and
light wind from the west.
Not a cloud in sight. **Jollytown Gazette**

## Sir Henry's Trophy Found

### by George Page, reporter

According to Police Officer Wong, Sir Henry's trophy has been found. Information will be shared at the Jollytown Community Hall tomorrow at 8:00 a.m.

People from all over gathered at the community hall to find out what had happened to my trophy. Officer Wong opened the meeting.

| | |
|---|---|
| *Officer Wong:* | Good morning. I am happy to report that Sir Henry's Best in Show trophy has been found. |
| | It was on the front desk of the Jollytown Police Station. Any questions? |
| *Reporter:* | Officer, why was the trophy at the police station? |
| *Officer Wong:* | It was the clerk's birthday. |
| *Reporter:* | What does that have to do with the missing trophy? |
| *Officer Wong:* | Orange roses were in the trophy. |
| *Reporter:* | But what were the roses doing in the trophy? |
| *Officer Wong:* | Let me tell you about the chain of events. |

Where was the trophy found? We don't know how the roses got in the trophy or how the trophy got to the police station. What do you think happened?

## FRIDAY, SEPTEMBER 17

- Sir Henry and John return home from victory walk.
- Trophy left on dining room table.
- Mrs. White bumps the trophy.
- Trophy falls into rummage sale box.

## SATURDAY, SEPTEMBER 18

- White family reports trophy missing.
- Florist buys trophy at rummage sale for one dollar, thinking it is a vase.
- Florist puts trophy on shelf with other vases.
- Florist gets call for 12 orange roses.
- Florist selects silver vase.
- Florist delivers orange roses to the police station for the clerk's birthday.

## SUNDAY, SEPTEMBER 19

- Officer Wong leads search party.
- Sir Henry and John retrace steps.
- Dog discovers trophy with orange flowers in it at the police station.

This chart shows the *chain of events*. What do you think that means? How did the trophy end up in the rummage sale box? Who thought the trophy was a vase? What happened next?

## Chapter 6

# Six Years Later

How has Sir Henry's life been *eventful*? What do you think he and John are doing six years after the trophy was won, lost, and found?

It's been six years since I won my first contest. The trophy case is now full. There are oodles of ribbons and six trophies—five for State and one for National Best in Show.

The White family and the whole community are proud of me. I am proud of me.

John and I still go for walks around our neighborhood. I'm older and slower now. Our little community has changed. There are a few more tall buildings. The vet has moved to a new office, and the florist is so busy that he had to get a bigger shop. Orange roses in trophy vases are very popular.

John spends a lot of time on the computer. He sends my pictures to dog lovers all over the country. I think he is writing a book about me. Awesome!

What's happened in the six years since Sir Henry won his first trophy?

I often think back to that day when I won my first trophy. I am grateful that I live in such a wonderful community. Without everyone's help, I couldn't have won the trophy. Without my community's help finding the trophy, I'd probably still be sulking in the corner.

Why is Sir Henry grateful that he lives where he does? Did you like the story about Sir Henry? Why or why not?

# Story Retell

## Sir Henry

Who told this story?

Where did most of the story take place?

---

● At the beginning, what did Sir Henry want?

---

■ In the middle of the story, a problem developed. What was the problem?

What actions did the characters take to solve the problem? What was the outcome?

---

▲ How was the mystery solved?

What lessons did Sir Henry learn about his community?

# Fluency

## E-Mail 1

*by Ann Watanabe and Marilyn Sprick*
*illustrated by Janet Pederson*

To: Sir Henry
Subject: Congratulations

Hey Henry, 2

Thanks for sending the news clippings. 8
Sorry I wasn't around to help you find your 17
trophy. What a commotion! Best in Show, a 25
victory, then the trophy goes missing. What a 33
chain of events! 36

You must have been distressed. That 42
Officer Wong is good, but she needs a detective 51
dog. She needs me. That's what she needs. 59
Those humans just don't have what it takes. I've 68
never seen them put their noses to the ground. 77

I would have sniffed us right to the trophy. 9

I would have dazzled Wong with my nose work. 18

Oh well—glad you got the trophy back! 26

I'm on a case searching for a colony of ants. 36
The scientists think it's fun to study ants. I find 46
that strange. I have been on the ant trail for 56
days. It's hot, dusty work. I am exhausted at 65
the end of the day, but it pays well. 74

What's next? Are you going for the gold? 82
You'll have to train hard. It's a good thing the 92
Jollytown dog groomers are so cool. Do they 100
still have those awesome treats? 105

Glad you aren't sulking in the corner 112
anymore. 113

Your detective brother, 116
Sir Winston 118

---

Describe Sir Winston. How is Sir Winston different from Sir Henry?

# Fluency

## E-Mail 2

*by Ann Watanabe and Marilyn Sprick*
*illustrated by Janet Pederson*

To: Sir Henry
Subject: Congratulations

Dear Brother Henry,                                                3

    Thank you for sending the news clippings.        10
I am so glad that you got your trophy back.                        20

    I read every news story to my class.              28
Officer Wong did a wonderful job organizing                        35
the search party.  Oh my, a lot of people from                     45
the community helped out—the barber, the                           52
groomer, the florist, and even the librarian.                      59

    It was a good lesson for my students.             67
The kittens and the pups were impressed                            74
with how helpful the humans were.  People in                       82
communities help each other out!  The pups did                     90
ask why Officer Wong didn't have a detective                       98
dog.  I thought that was a very good question.                     107

I have a delightful class. The pups are 8
learning how to walk on leash. It isn't a popular 18
lesson, but they are getting very good. I told 27
them they could be like you one day—Best in 37
Show. The kittens are learning how to use the 46
litter box. Oh yes, they are all learning 54
important skills! 56

Most of all, we like our reading lessons. 64
We are reading stories about a dog detective. 72
The dog reminds me of Winston. 78

Keep in touch, brother dear. 83

Your loving sister, 86
Lady Elizabeth 88

Describe Lady Elizabeth. How is Lady Elizabeth different from Sir Winston?

# UNIT 7
# Stories From Hilo

# Miss Tam in Hilo

*by Karen Akiyama-Paik,
Ann Watanabe, and Marilyn Sprick
illustrated by Page Eastburn O'Rourke*

Who is this story about? Describe Miss Tam. What do you think she will do in this story?

# Vocabulary

## im·pressed

To be **impressed** means to think someone does something really well.

Miss Tam was *impressed* by how the women in Ghana carried things on their heads. Why was she impressed?

## ★ tat·tered

**Tattered** means old, torn, or worn out. Books, papers, and clothes can become tattered.

I had a pair of *tattered* jeans that I loved. Use the word *tattered* to describe something you might have.

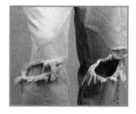

## cus·tom

A **custom** is a way of doing something. Often a group of people shares the same customs.

It is a *custom* for people in Hawaii to take and bring back gifts from their travels. If someone brought you a gift from Hawaii, what would you want?

What custom do you see in the picture?

★ = New

64

## ★ ex·haust·ing

Something that makes you really, really tired is **exhausting**.

Miss Tam's long plane ride to Ghana was *exhausting*. How did she feel at the end of her plane ride?

## ★ splen·did

Something that is great, outstanding, or terrific is **splendid**.

The sunset was a *splendid* sight. What does that tell us about the sunset?

## lo·cal

**Local** describes things and places close to your home or community.

Miss Tam buys birdseed at the *local* pet store. Where is the pet store?

## Chapter 1

# The Pearly White Hatpin

What do you think the pearly white hatpin has to do with Miss Tam's travels?

At exactly 7:00 a.m., Miss Tam said, "Mah-chee (maw-chee), mah-chee, Minnie Bird. Good morning."

Minnie Bird screeched back, "Mah-chee, mah-chee."

Miss Tam said, "Nice job, Minnie Bird! My friends in Ghana would be impressed."

What is Miss Tam teaching Minnie Bird? Why would the people in Ghana be *impressed*?

Old Scraggly Cat just opened one eye and closed it again.

Then, as was her habit, Miss Tam put on her slippers with the pink puffballs. At exactly 7:30 a.m., Miss Tam, Old Scraggly Cat, and Minnie Bird sat down to their breakfasts. Miss Tam was settling into another ordinary and restful day.

At 8:30 a.m., Miss Tam picked up her mail and the newspaper. In the stack of mail was a postcard.

Miss Tam said, "Well, I'll be!" Then Miss Tam pulled out a tattered world map and carefully taped it to the wall.

"Look," said Miss Tam as she stuck a bright red hatpin into the map. "This is Montgomery, where we live." Old Scraggly Cat purred.

Then Miss Tam stuck a blue hatpin in Africa and said, "This is Ghana. And this," said Miss Tam, "is where I'm going next."

---

What did Miss Tam get in the mail? What is Miss Tam doing with the hatpins? What do you think she will do with the pearly white hatpin?

Then Miss Tam stuck a pearly white hatpin into an island in the Pacific Ocean. Miss Tam was going to Hawaii. Minnie Bird squawked, "Ha ha!"

What kind of map did Miss Tam put on her wall? Touch Montgomery. What does the white hatpin show?

Miss Tam said, "Maybe I can learn to dance the hula!  Maybe I can learn to surf!"

Minnie Bird said, "Uh oh," and Old Scraggly Cat put his paws over his eyes.

Miss Tam said, "It will be great.  I will bring you omiyage (oh-me-yah-gay)."

OUTRIGGER CANOE IN HILO, HAWAII

Aloha, Miss Tam!

Congratulations on your retirement. Come and visit me in Hilo. We must celebrate Hawaiian-style.

Love, Aunty Lani

Miss Tam
85 Read Well St.
Montgomery, AL   12345

What did Minnie Bird say when Miss Tam said she might learn to surf?  Why do you think Old Scraggly Cat put his paws over his eyes?  What do you think omiyage is?

## Chapter 2

# Off to Hawaii

Soon Miss Tam was packing for Hawaii. The last thing that went in Miss Tam's travel bag was a box of grits for her dear friend Aunty Lani.

"This is omiyage (oh-me-yah-gay)," said Miss Tam.

Minnie Bird screeched, "Oh-me-yah-gay, oh-me-yah-gay!"

"Yes, Minnie Bird," said Miss Tam. "Aunty Lani would be so impressed that you know the word omiyage.

"You are getting very smart, Minnie Bird. Giving omiyage is a custom in Hawaii. People take and bring back gifts from their travels. I will bring you back a gift from my travels."

Minnie Bird squawked, "Gift? Gift?"

Miss Tam was sad to leave Minnie Bird and Old Scraggly Cat, but she was excited to go to Hawaii.

---

What makes it seem like Minnie Bird is getting smarter? What is Miss Tam's gift for Aunty Lani?

After a long and exhausting journey, Miss Tam landed in Hilo. "Aloha, Miss Tam!" said Aunty Lani. Then she gave Miss Tam a beautiful flower lei (lay) and a huge hug.

Miss Tam said, "Oh, the lei is splendid!"

What was the omiyage Aunty Lani gave to Miss Tam?

It wasn't long before Miss Tam noticed the warm air in Hilo. She looked down at her hot feet. She had on her sturdy brown walking shoes. Miss Tam asked, "Could we shop for flip-flops?"

Aunty Lani said, "You mean slippers."

"No," insisted Miss Tam. "I have lovely pink slippers at home. I need flip-flops."

Aunty Lani chuckled. "In Hawaii, flip-flops are called slippers." Aunty Lani held up her foot so Miss Tam could see her bright pink rubber slippers.

Miss Tam grinned. "Slippers!"

Aunty Lani said, "First stop, Short's Drug Store. That's where the local folk buy slippers." Soon Miss Tam's feet were flip-flopping across the parking lot.

What did Miss Tam buy for herself in Hilo? Why did she need slippers?

## Chapters 3, 4

# Vocabulary

### bar·gain

When you **bargain**, you try to pay less for something than the seller's price.

*My mom likes to bargain for good deals when she goes to garage sales. What does that mean?*

### ★ un·set·tled

When someone is a little worried or nervous, he or she may feel **unsettled**.

*Sir Henry felt unsettled when his trophy disappeared. What does that mean? Have you ever felt unsettled?*

### ★ fas·ci·nat·ed

To be **fascinated** means to find something or someone very interesting.

*Miss Tam was fascinated by the hippos in Africa. What does that mean? What are you fascinated by?*

★ = New

74

★ **con·tent·ed**

**Contented** means happy.

Old Scraggly Cat was *contented* after having a breakfast of grits a ham. Why did Old Scraggly Cat purr contentedly?

★ **sway**

**Sway** means to move slowly and smoothly from side to side.

The trees *swayed* gently in the breeze. Show me what it looks like to sway.

★ **gen·er·a·tion**

Within a family, there are grandparents, parents, and children. Each group is called a **generation**.

All of you are a *generation*. Your parents are another generation, and your grandparents are another generation. Point to someone in your generation.

## Chapter 3

# The Farmer's Market

Look at the picture and think about the chapter title. What do you think Miss Tam will do in Hawaii?

Miss Tam's week in Hawaii flew by. She visited a rain forest, walked on a black sand beach, went snorkeling in the sea, and hiked to a beautiful waterfall. She also ate lots of splendid food.

On Saturday, Miss Tam went to the local farmer's market. There were oodles of fresh vegetables and fruits, colorful flowers, jams, and cakes. People were selling, buying, bargaining, and telling stories. The market reminded Miss Tam of Ghana.

SNORKELING IN HILO, HAWAII

Dear Old Scraggly Cat,
I have been eating
and eating and eating.
You would like the
raw fish.
I miss you.
Love, Miss Tam

Old Scraggly Cat
85 F
Mo
123

Dear Minnie Bird,
I saw some of
your relatives in
the rain forest.
I miss you!
Love, Miss Tam

Minnie Bird
85 Read Well St.
Montgomery, AL
12345

What did Miss Tam do while she was in Hawaii? Why did the market remind Miss Tam of Ghana?

Aunty Lani said that almost everyone in the community shopped at the farmer's market.

Miss Tam thought that Aunty Lani knew everyone.

"Mrs. Soon! How are your fresh long beans?" asked Aunty Lani.

As she strolled through the market, Aunty Lani stopped every few feet. "Hey, Josh. I need four fresh fish today. Hello, Mrs. Lee. How much for the eggplant?"

Why did Miss Tam think Aunty Lani knew everyone?

Miss Tam bought pepper jelly and coconut bowls—omiyage for Mr. Moffitt and her many friends at home.

Miss Tam stayed at one booth for a long time, admiring the beautiful handmade goods. Finally, she bought herself a pillowcase. It wasn't any ordinary pillowcase. It was made from a lovely handmade Hawaiian quilt.

Miss Tam was very happy. However, as she got in the car, she had an unsettled feeling. Miss Tam thought, "I've forgotten someone's omiyage. Who could it be?"

What is omiyage? Why does Miss Tam feel *unsettled*?

## Chapter 4

# The Community

What has Miss Tam done in Hawaii? What else do you think she will do?

On Sunday, Aunty Lani drove Miss Tam to the volcano. The land was black, and steam rose from vents in the ground. Miss Tam was fascinated.

Aunty Lani said, "Stay on the trails, and it is very safe. Just don't take any lava rock. Some people say it will bring bad luck."

Describe what Miss Tam saw on her visit to the volcano.

On Sunday, Aunty Lani's family and neighbors gathered for dinner—just as they did every Sunday. Miss Tam helped set up tables and chairs in the garage.

Everyone ate, talked, and sang. Miss Tam ate her favorite rice balls, and she even danced the hula. She learned how to sway her hips and use her hands to show the gently falling rain. As she danced, Miss Tam thought, "Ha ha!" She knew whose omiyage she had forgotten.

Before the evening was over, the children gathered around Aunty Lani to hear the ancient stories of Hawaii. Aunty Lani said, "Listen carefully, so you can tell our stories to your children." Then, as generations before her had, Aunty Lani told the legend of Pele (Pay-lay), the goddess of the volcano.

The next morning, Miss Tam got ready to go home. Saying goodbye to Aunty Lani and her new friends was bittersweet. On the way to the airport, Miss Tam bought the last of her omiyage.

---

Why do people in Hawaii say not to take the lava rock? Where did Aunty Lani's family and neighbors gather for dinner? What happened at the *neighborhood* gathering?

Then Miss Tam got on a plane and headed contentedly back home across the ocean.

Hours and hours later, Miss Tam was opening her door. Minnie Bird screeched, "Good day!"

Miss Tam said, "Aloha."

Minnie Bird screeched back, "Aloha!"

Miss Tam smiled and petted Old Scraggly Cat. It was good to be home.

---

What was the last thing Miss Tam did before she went to the airport? Who do you think she bought the last omiyage for?

What did Miss Tam bring home for Minnie Bird and Old Scraggly Cat? How do you think they feel about their omiyage?

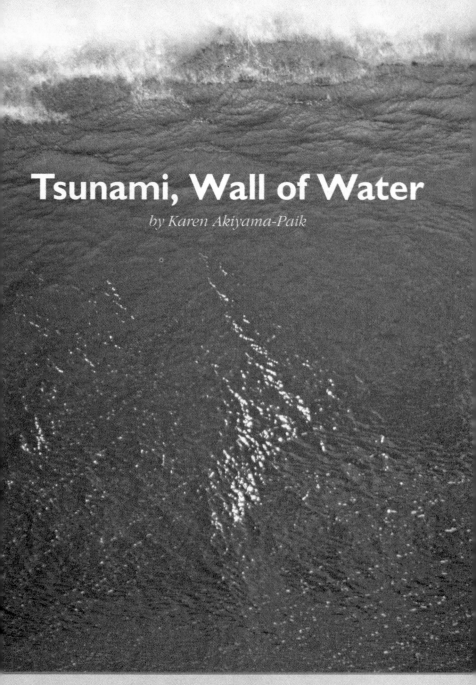

# Tsunami, Wall of Water

*by Karen Akiyama-Paik*

This shows a huge wave called a tsunami.  A tsunami may be as tall as a 10-story building.

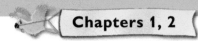

**Chapters 1, 2**

# Vocabulary

★ **na·tur·al di·sas·ter**

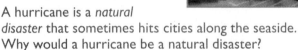

A **natural disaster** is a sudden thing that happens in nature. A natural disaster causes great damage.

A hurricane is a *natural disaster* that sometimes hits cities along the seaside. Why would a hurricane be a natural disaster?

★ **vi·bra·tion**

A **vibration** is a shaking movement that you can feel.

I could feel the *vibration* from the jackhammer. Can you imagine how it would feel to hold a jackhammer?

★ **sur·face**

A **surface** is the top layer of something.

Fish swim under the *surface* of the water. Look at the picture. Where are the fish swimming? Touch the surface.

★ = New

## ★ de·stroy

**Destroy** means to damage something so badly that it is completely wiped out.

The flood *destroyed* the house. What's another way to say "The hurricane wiped out the whole town"? Start with "The hurricane . . ."

## sur·vive

**Survive** means to stay alive.

Many of the animals *survived* the cold winter. If you lived through a terrible storm, what could you say? Use the word *survived*.

## Idioms and Expressions

## ★ false a·larm

An alarm is a warning about something. A **false alarm** is a warning about something that does not happen.

Everyone thought there was a fire, but it was a *false alarm.* The alarm had been set off by mistake. What's another way to say that the news of a tiger running loose was not true?

## Chapter 1

# Natural Disasters

What are some natural disasters that you've heard about?

Around the world, volcanoes suddenly erupt, and lava flows across the land. Earthquakes rumble, hurricanes blow, and rivers flood. These things are called natural disasters. During a natural disaster, ordinary people become heroes, and people help each other.

Communities work together.

What is a *natural disaster*? What do communities do when there's a disaster?

## Waves Deep in the Sea

A tsunami (tsoo-nah-me) is a natural disaster that sometimes hits communities near the sea. A tsunami is a group of waves that travels deep under the water.

Although a tsunami is a group of waves, these are not ordinary waves. Ordinary waves are caused by wind. A tsunami usually begins with the vibrations of an earthquake in or near the sea. The waves can travel thousands of miles before they reach land.

When the waves travel through deep water, they cannot be seen on the surface. They travel as fast as an airplane! When a tsunami crashes ashore, it is like a giant wall of water. These giant waves can be higher than a 10-story building!

How does a tsunami begin? How big can a tsunami be?

## Tsunamis in Hilo

Over the years, the community in Hilo, Hawaii, has been struck by many tsunamis. On April 1, 1946, on the big island of Hawaii, fishermen were getting their morning catch. All of a sudden, the sea rushed out, leaving their boats stuck in the sand. Within minutes, a huge wave crashed on shore. More waves followed. The tsunami destroyed much of the town of Hilo. The tsunami had traveled 2,400 miles from an earthquake near Alaska before hitting the little island community.

Describe what happened in Hilo in 1946.

On May 22, 1960, a huge earthquake shook Chile, a faraway country on the continent of South America. Fifteen hours later, that earthquake caused another tsunami in Hilo. First, the sea rushed out, leaving boats stuck in the sand. Then, several minutes later, giant waves hit the shore. To this day, the community in Hilo still talks about the tsunami of 1960. They have many stories to tell about people who helped and people who survived.

Describe what happened in Hilo on 1960. What was the same about the tsunami in 1946 and the tsunami in 1960?

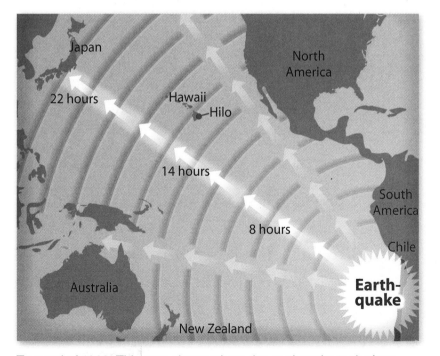

Tsunami of 1960: This map shows where the earthquake took place. The dark blue bands show how long it took the waves to reach Hawaii.

 **Chapter 2**

# Surviving Tsunamis

What does it mean to *survive* a tsunami?

### Mrs. Ito's Story

It was May 22, 1960—just an ordinary day in Hilo. Mrs. Ito (Eee-toe) was at home when the afternoon news warned of danger. A tsunami was coming at 12:30 that night.

Mrs. Ito worried about the town, but not about herself. The tsunami of 1946 had not reached her home. Mrs. Ito thought she would be safe. She listened to the news, but 12:30 came and went.

Mrs. Ito saw people going back to their homes. The tsunami wasn't coming—false alarm. Then suddenly, a thunderous sound filled the air, and a giant wave crashed into Mrs. Ito's house.

Mrs. Ito found herself floating in the sea with branches, trash, and even a chair. Hours later, Mrs. Ito saw two boats. People were waving at her. You can imagine how Mrs. Ito felt. When she was safely on the boat, she was very happy. She was safe!

Why wasn't Mrs. Ito worried about the tsunami warning? Why did Mrs. Ito find herself in the ocean? When did Mrs. Ito feel safe and happy?

Mrs. Ito was happy to have survived the tsunami that destroyed parts of Hilo in 1960.

## Tsunami Watch

After the tsunami of 1960, the people of Hawaii built the Pacific Tsunami Warning Center. There, scientists watch for large vibrations under the ocean. Those vibrations can mean an earthquake has happened. If the earthquake is big, the scientists tell people that a tsunami could be coming. When communities know a big wave is coming, they may have time to move people to safety. It takes teamwork, but lives can be saved.

## Help Around the World

In times of disaster, it isn't only the local community that pulls together. The world community helps too. People send money, food, and clothing to people who have survived hurricanes, tsunamis, floods, and earthquakes. When a natural disaster strikes, anyone and everyone can help.

> People in communities work together to solve problems.

> People in the world community work together to solve problems.

What do scientists watch for? How are people in Hawaii safer now? If a natural disaster hits, how could you help?

# Fluency

## Miss Tam's Scrapbook

*by Karen Akiyama-Paik*
*illustrated by Page Eastburn O'Rourke*

Miss Tam sat at her kitchen table with
a bowl of red beans and rice. A scrapbook
was open on the table. She wore her old pink
slippers and a lei around her neck. Miss Tam
looked at a picture of herself standing next to
a clock near Hilo Bay.

The clock in the picture had stopped when
the tsunami of 1960 hit. Miss Tam thought to
herself, "I need to tell Mr. Moffitt all about the
big wave that hit Hilo. He will be fascinated."

# Fluency

Then Miss Tam turned the page of the 8
scrapbook.  There she was with a face mask and 17
fins.  Minnie Bird squawked, "Dear, dear!  What 24
a sight." 26

Miss Tam chuckled.  "My friends at the 33
library must see this picture.  They won't believe 41
that I went snorkeling." 45

Then Miss Tam turned to the next page in 54
her scrapbook.  There she was, eating a rice ball. 63
The rice ball was wrapped with seaweed.  Minnie 71
Bird squawked, "Seaweed?" 74

Miss Tam said, "Yes, delicious!"  Old 80
Scraggly Cat purred. 83

When Miss Tam reached the last page, she 91
laughed out loud.  There were Old Scraggly Cat 99
and Minnie Bird, all dressed up in grass skirts 108
and lei. 110

Miss Tam couldn't wait to go to the library. 119
Mr. Moffitt would be delighted to see and hear all 129
about her adventures in Hilo. 134

## bargain

When you **bargain**, you try to pay less for something than the seller's price.

My mom likes to *bargain* for good deals when she goes to yard sales.

## collapse

**Collapse** means to fall down suddenly and completely.

The tower of blocks kept *collapsing*.

## colony

A **colony** is a group of animals that lives together.

Thousands of ants live together in a *colony*.

## commotion

A **commotion** is a lot of noise and activity.

Dad did not like the *commotion* we made with our music.

## community

A **community** is a group of people or animals that lives and works together.

Our school is a *community*.

## congratulate

**Congratulate** means to tell others you are happy for them because they won something or did something special.

The principal *congratulated* the student for reading 100 books.

## contented

**Contented** means happy.

Old Scraggly Cat was *contented* after having a breakfast of grits and ham.

## custom

A **custom** is a way of doing something. Often a group of people shares the same customs.

It is a *custom* for people in the United States to shake hands.

## dawdle

**Dawdle** means to do something slowly.

Sometimes, I *dawdle* on my way to school.

## delightful

**Delightful** means cheerful and fun.

He is a *delightful* child.

## destroy

**Destroy** means to damage something so badly that it is completely wiped out.

The fire *destroyed* the building.

## distressed

**Distressed** means very upset.

The girl was *distressed* when she lost her dog.

## except

**Except** is a short way of saying "everything but" or "everywhere but."

I like all vegetables *except* broccoli.

## exhausted

**Exhausted** means very tired.

The baby was *exhausted* after visiting the relatives.

## fascinated

To be **fascinated** means to find something or someone very interesting.

Miss Tam was *fascinated* by the hippos in Africa.

# Glossary

## generation

Within a family, there are grandparents, parents, and children. Each group is called a **generation**.

Your parents are one *generation*, and your grandparents are another generation.

## habitat

The place where an animal or plant lives and grows is called its **habitat**.

A hippo's *habitat* is near rivers in Africa.

## imagination

If you can think of new ideas or stories, you have **imagination**.

Inventors have great *imagination*.

## impressed

To be **impressed** means to think someone does something really well.

Tim was *impressed* with Maria's new magic trick.

## life cycle

From birth to death, plants and animals go through changes. These changes, or stages, are called a **life cycle**.

The *life cycle* of many insects has four stages: 1) egg, 2) larva, 3) pupa, 4) adult.

## local

Local describes things and places close to your home or community.

A *local* school is a school close to your home.

## metamorphosis

Metamorphosis is a big change that some animals go through during their life cycle.

A tadpole goes through a *metamorphosis* by changing from a tadpole into a frog.

## molt

When animals shed their skin, they **molt**.

Snakes and caterpillars *molt*.

## natural disaster

A **natural disaster** is a sudden thing that happens in nature. A natural disaster causes great damage.

The hurricane was a *natural disaster* that hit cities along the seaside.

## plead

Plead means to beg. When you really want something, you may beg, or plead, for it.

The boy *pleaded* with his mom to let him stay up late.

# Glossary

## popular

Something is **popular** when many people like it.

*Our local restaurant is very popular.*

## protect

**Protect** means to keep safe.

*Mother animals protect their babies.*

## retrace

**Retrace** means to go back and do something again. When you retrace your steps, you go back exactly the way you came.

*I lost my ring and retraced my steps to find it.*

## splendid

Something that is great, outstanding, or terrific is **splendid**.

*The sunset was a splendid sight.*

## sulk

**Sulk** means to show that you are unhappy. People often sulk by pouting and not talking.

*He was so unhappy that he sulked.*

## surface

A **surface** is the top layer of something.

Fish swim under the *surface* of the water.

## survive

**Survive** means to stay alive.

Many of the animals *survived* the cold winter.

## sway

**Sway** means to move slowly and smoothly from side to side.

The trees *swayed* gently in the breeze.

## tattered

**Tattered** means old, torn, or worn out. Books, papers, and clothes can become tattered.

I had a *tattered* pair of jeans that I loved.

## treasure

A **treasure** is something valuable or important. A treasure is often money, jewels, or gold, but it can be anything you think is important.

The pirate's *treasure* was a chest of gold.

# Glossary

## unsettled

When someone is a little worried or nervous, he or she may feel **unsettled**.

Sir Henry felt *unsettled* when his trophy disappeared.

## vibration

A **vibration** is a shaking movement that you can feel.

I could feel the *vibration* from the jackhammer.

## victory

A **victory** is a win.

When the girl won the race, it was a sweet *victory*.

## Idioms and Expressions

## chain of events

A **chain of events** is a series of things that happen in a certain order. Each thing causes the next thing to happen.

Minnie Bird screeched. Then Miss Tam jumped and spilled the milk. It was quite a *chain of events*.

## false alarm

An alarm is a warning about something. A **false alarm** is a warning about something that does not happen.

Everyone thought there was a fire, but it was a *false alarm*.